THE
SESAME STREET®
LIBRARY

With Jim Henson's Muppets

VOLUME 12

FEATURING
THE LETTERS
W, X, Y AND Z
AND THE NUMBER
12

Children's Television Workshop/Funk & Wagnalls, Inc.

WRITTEN BY:

Michael Frith
Jerry Juhl
Emily Perl Kingsley
Sharon Lerner
Nina B. Link
Albert G. Miller
Jeffrey Moss
Norman Stiles
Jon Stone
Daniel Wilcox

ILLUSTRATED BY:

Mel Crawford
A. Delaney
Michael Frith
David Gantz
Joseph Mathieu
Jon McIntosh
Marc Nadel
Kelly Oechsli
Michael J. Smollin

PHOTOGRAPHS BY:

Charles P. Rowan

Snuffie Learns the Alphabet
by Big Bird

When Mr. Snuffle-upagus
   was just a little kid
He had a great big problem,
   And this is what he did.
He came one day and said to me,
   "I've found this big, long word.
I don't know how to say it, though—
   Can you explain it, Bird?"

I took that piece of paper,
   I looked at it and smiled,
"I used to make the same mistake
   When I was just a child.

"This thing is not a word at all—
   It's called the ALPHABET.
Just say each letter separately,
   And *this* is what you'll get..."

ABCD...EFG
HIJK...LMNOP
QRS...TUV
WX...Y...Z

O.K., now, say this along with me, and we'll teach Mr. Snuffle-upagus how the Alphabet goes.

"I think that you know
EVERYTHING,"
I heard my friend Snuff say.
"When did *you* learn the
   Alphabet?"

Oh... I learned it yesterday.

L M N O P

Grover Gets Wet

Hi! It is your
old pal Grover
again, here to
talk to you about
the letter **W**.

Do you know what begins
with the letter **W**?
Water begins with the
letter **W**. And this is
a big tank of water.

Do you know who lives in this
tank of water? Willy the Walrus
lives in this tank of water.
And his name begins with the
letter **W**, too. Oh, this is so much fun.

I will now bend over
the top of the tank
and see if my cute
little eyes can see
Willy the Walrus.

WHOOPS!

Whoops also
starts with
the letter W.

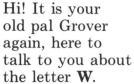

Now I am wet. The word **wet**
begins with the letter **W**. Well,
since I am wet, there is one
other thing that begins with
the letter **W** . . .

WASH!

Ernie Buys a 12

One morning, as Ernie was walking home from Mr. Hooper's store with a box of eggs for breakfast, he heard a mysterious voice...

Roosevelt Franklin Plays
GUESS WHAT I FOUND

Remember that groovy game Roosevelt Franklin taught you called GUESS WHAT I FOUND in Volume 4? You won't believe this, but you can play that <u>same game</u> using colors. Too much!

The first player looks around, chooses something red, and says, "I looked around, and guess what I found. I found something red." He might choose a red book, or a red pencil, or even somebody's red shirt.

The other players try to guess what he found. The one who guesses right gets to choose the next color . . . like, "I looked around, and guess what I found. I found something YELLOW." Out of sight!

Roosevelt Franklin sure likes this game! You just keep on playing until you've used up all of the colors you can. Then you can start all over again.

Here are some good colors to look for.

red   green   blue   yellow

Rapunzel

Once a wicked old witch kept a beautiful
girl named Rapunzel locked up in a tower. There
were no stairs leading up to the tower, and no
one else was allowed to see the girl. Every night
when the witch came home she would cry:
"Rapunzel! Let down your hair!"

Then Rapunzel would lean out of the window
and let down her long yellow braid so the witch
could climb up to the tower.

One moonlit night a prince saw the
beautiful girl in the tower. When he was sure
the witch was not home he decided to visit
the girl.

"Rapunzel! Let down your hair!" he cried.
Rapunzel was very happy to see someone
other than the witch. But when the wicked witch
heard about the prince, she was angry. She cut
off Rapunzel's hair and took her away to
the woods.

When the prince returned the next night,
the witch let down the long braid that she had
shorn from Rapunzel's head. The prince climbed
up. But when he reached the top he was so
surprised to see the old witch instead of
Rapunzel that he let go and fell to the ground.

Luckily, Rapunzel was there and together
they ran far away. Soon they were wed, living
happily ever after.

I have this poem here about body parts.
My friends are going to show you what they are.

Ankle, Shoulder, Knee
by Big Bird

Oh! A knee is kinda roundish, like an orange or an egg;
You'll find it sticking out, right in the middle of your leg.
It bends right in the middle when you want to run or jump;
It's a funny kinda, lumpy kinda, knobby kinda bump.

Oh! A B C D – 1, 2, 3,
Let's all sing a song about a knee!

Oh! A shoulder is the joint that's at the top part of your arm,
And everybody's got 'em, in the city or the farm.
It's so useful when you want to wave hello or wave good-bye,
And wiggling it up and down is easy if you try.

Oh! A B C – When you are older,
Hope you'll remember this song about a shoulder.

Oh! An ankle can be found at the beginning of your foot,
And when you're getting dressed, it's in the sock that it is put.
An ankle is important if you want to dance or run,
And if anybody kicks you there, it isn't any fun.

Oh! A B C – A jinkle and a jankle,
It's hard to find a rhyme
For a silly word like ankle.

When you think about your body
And you think of all its parts,
Don't only think of eyes and ears,
Of noses, mouths, and hearts...
Think of the parts that move and bend,
That help both you and me
To walk and run and jump and play—
The ankle, shoulder, knee.

Oh! 8, 9, 10, W X Y Z—
That's all we have to say abou
The ankle, shoulder, knee.
Wheeee

THE MAGIC APPLE

There was once a simple farm boy,
Poor but honest as the dickens,
And he worked from dawn to midnight,
Pitching hay and feeding chickens.
"I am poor and I am honest,"
Said the farm boy, "but it's rough
Working every day till midnight
Pitching hay and other stuff."

Thought the poor but honest farm boy,
As he leaned upon his rake,
"If I had one wish to wish for,
There is only one I'd make.
I would wish to trade this barnyard
And this yucchy farm-boy life,
For a dandy golden palace
And a princess for a wife."

He was sound asleep one morning
Underneath an apple tree,
When he heard a great explosion
That was loud as it could be.
BOOM! A lady stood beside him,
Saying, "Hello there, young fella.
I'm your handy fairy god-ma,
Like the one in Cinderella."

"Pleased to meet you," said her godson,
As he grinned from ear to ear.
"You're a mighty pretty lady
And I'm glad to see you here."
"Sonny," said the pretty lady,
"I've a big surprise for you:
If there's anything you wish for,
I will see that it comes true."

"Hey, that's groovy!" said the farm boy,
"Golly, I can hardly wait!"
"*One* wish only," said the fairy,
"So you'd better make it great."
Said the boy, "*Two* things I wish for,
Either one and I'd be lucky:
One's a nice banana milkshake . . .
One's a brand new rubber duckie."

"Wait a minute! Are you crazy?
Have you changed your mind?" she cried.
"What you wanted was a palace
And a princess for a bride."
"You're so right, ma'am," said her godson,
"But I think that I'd be lucky
If the palace had a princess,
AND a milkshake, AND a duckie."

"It's a deal," the fairy answered,
Pointing upward in the tree.
"If you pick that magic apple,
What you wish will come to be."
Then there came a loud explosion,
And before her godson spoke,
She had vanished very quickly
In a cloud of purple smoke.

"I can't reach that magic apple,"
Said the farm boy. "Not at all."
So he grabbed the tree and shook it,
But the apple wouldn't fall.

Then he got so tired from shaking
That he tumbled in a heap
Underneath the magic apple,
Where he promptly fell asleep.

Then his snoring shook the tree trunk
From the bottom to the top,
And the rosy magic apple
Fell into his mouth—KER-PLOP!

"Glugga-mugga," said the farm boy,
"Argha-bargha, google-gapple."
But you couldn't understand him
'Cause his mouth was full of apple.

For awhile he lay there gurgling,
Making lots of silly talk,
Then a wealthy king came strolling
On his daily royal walk.
"Say there, poor but honest farm boy,"
Said the king, "I beg your pardon,
But is that a *magic* apple?"
Said the boy, "Blub-garfer-gardon."

Said his majesty, "I'm sorry,
But I do not understand."
So the boy took out the apple
And he held it in his hand.
"Sure, this apple's *full* of magic,"
Said the boy. "It's *got* to be,
'Cause my fairy god-ma said so,
Underneath this very tree."

"I've been looking for a farm boy
(Poor but honest) since the spring,
Who possessed a magic apple,"
Said the very happy king.
"Will you move into my palace
And be married to my daughter?
You will have your own apartment
With a stove and running water."

"Will I have banana milkshakes,
And some rubber duckies, too?"
"Why of course," replied the monarch,
"I'll have tons of *both* for you."
"Then I'll do it," said the farm boy.
"Where's the princess I'm to wed?"
"She is waiting at the castle.
Come with me," the monarch said.

When the farm boy saw the princess,
Everybody heard his screams,
For she didn't look exactly
Like the princess of his dreams.
But with duckies and with milkshakes
He lived all his life in clover.
Isn't that a lovely story?
Are you sorry that it's over?

Ernie
Makes A Statue

OSCAR CHOOSES A PET

"I've been thinking," Oscar muttered,
"Of the pleasant life I lead,
Living in this filthy trashcan—
It is very nice indeed!

But it might be even better
If I had a little pet,
Though it's kind of hard to figure
Just what animal to get."

"I could never think of puppies,
'Cause they wag their tails all day,
And they're lovable and darling,
So I'd hate them right away.

Tiny kittens are no better,
For they're cute, beyond a doubt,
And they're always washing whiskers,
So the kittens, man, are out."

Oscar thought another minute,
Then he almost flipped his wig.
"Holy smoke!" he cried, "I've got it!
I will buy myself a *pig!*

Since a pig is fat and filthy,
I would love him like a cousin.
What a roommate for my trashcan!
Hey! I think I'll buy a *dozen!*"

What is blue and green and plays music?

The Grover and Oscar Marching Band.

The Amazing Mumford's Christmas Show

his is a picture of The Amazing
umford. He is about to perform
is most famous trick—pulling
a rabbit out of his hat.

Oh, dear. He seems to have
pulled out a RED ball...

...and a GREEN ball...

...and some YELLOW ribbon...
and a beautiful BLUE star.

MERRY
CHRISTMAS,
Mumfie!
And here's a nice
new WHITE
rabbit for
your hat.

With **ONE** egg cup
and four pipe cleaners
you can make a darling
spider . . .

And with **TWO** egg cups
and three pipe cleaners
and a cork you
can make
an adorable camel . . .

*you can hang
your bat with
a rubber band*

And with **THREE** egg cups
and no pipe cleaners you
can make a lovable bat . . .

And with **FOUR** egg cups
and one pipe cleaner
you can make an EXCITING
COUNTING GAME called
Twiddlywinks.

TWIDDLYWINKS

HOW TO MAKE IT
1. Make a Twiddlebug
out of paper or card-
board. (Use a pipe
cleaner for the feelers
and draw on the eyes,
mouth, and wings.)
2. Cut two slots in the
Twiddlebug and put a
toothpick through the
slots.
3. Cut out four connect-
ing sections of an egg
carton and stick the
Twiddlebug toothpick in
the center.

HOW TO PLAY IT
1. Collect 10 pennies or
buttons to use as tokens.
2. Put the Twiddle-cups
on a table or on the
floor, about two feet
from the players.
3. Each player takes a
turn and tries to toss the
10 tokens into the cups.
4. The player who gets
the most tokens into the
Twiddle-cups wins.

And with **FIVE** egg cups
and two pipe cleaners
you can make this
BEAUTIFUL caterpillar . . .

. . . Isn't it exciting? *Five marvelous toys!*

Well,
I have something
exciting for you.
ONE mop and **ONE** bucket
and I'd like to see that
ONE mess cleaned up before
I count to **THREE!**

Start counting!
Start counting!

How is it?   Yummy!

yY

There! Now this the **Y** page!
Now everything belong!
And you know something?
This letter *delicious!!*

YAY!
YAM
YOGURT!

YUMM-O
YOGURT

Cc

a cuddly cub

a candy cane

Dd

a darling doggie

a dozen dandelions

a b c d e f g h i j k l m n o p q r s t u v w x y z

If you want to make a book like mine, here's how to do it. First, find 14 pieces of paper.

Write your name on the first page. Then, using both sides of the paper, write a letter of the alphabet near the top of each of the other pages.

A

Now look through your old magazines and newspapers and cut out pictures of things that start with each letter.

Stick the things that start with A on the A page, and the B things on the B page, and so on.

GLUE

Ee

If you can't find a picture you like, you can draw one yourself.

t all the pages together, e a book. Punch two les in the side, like this.

Then, find some pretty ribbon or yarn, put it through the holes, and tie a bow. Then you'll have your very *own* "Lovely Letter Book."

Yucch! That's what I call a LOUSY letter book! Now, look at this . . . here are some mad monkeys munching on moldy marshmallows, and . . .

Mm

Ernie Buys a Z

As Ernie walked down the street one day, he heard a "Pssst!" from nearby. He looked around and saw a shifty-looking Salesman hiding behind a tree.

"C'mere, kid," said the Salesman. "I'm gonna show you something that'll save you pain and trouble." And out from under his coat he took a big letter **Z**.

"That's the letter **Z**," said Ernie. "How will it save me pain and trouble?"

I'll explain," said the Salesman. "Suppose you're at a party. And suppose somebody at the party asks you what the first letter is in the word **zebra**. And you can't remember."

"Oh, dear," said Ernie. He was imagining the party. He could just see it. Everybody would be pointing at him, and saying he couldn't spell. They'd probably never invite him to another party. If only he could remember the first letter in **zebra**!

"But," said the Salesman, "if you had this **Z**, you could take it out, look at it, and it would remind you that the first letter in **zebra** is **Z**."

"Thank goodness for that **Z**," said Ernie. "It's great for parties."

"Right," said the Salesman. "And there's another way it can help you. Suppose you're on a quiz show. The prize is two million dollars, *plus* a trip around the world, *and* a carton full of rubber duckies . . ."

"Wowee!" said Ernie. "What a prize!"

The Salesman went on, "Your question is: What's the first letter in the word **zoo**? But you can't remember. The seconds are ticking by . . .

. . . the band is playing tense music. . . ."

Ernie could just picture the whole thing. There he was, on the quiz show. If he couldn't answer the question, he'd get no prize! Everybody would boo him! If only he could remember the first letter in **zoo**!

"Well," said the Salesman, "if you had this **Z**, it would remind you that the first letter in zoo is **Z**."

"That settles it!" said Ernie. "I've got to have that **Z**! It'll save me pain and trouble!"

So Ernie bought the **Z** and walked away with it down the street.

The Salesman was about to leave when a stranger came up, holding a microphone. "HI!" he said. "I'm GUY SMILEY, and *you* are on QUIZ SHOW IN THE STREET! Today's prize is TWO MILLION DOLLARS, *PLUS* A TRIP AROUND THE WORLD, *AND* A CARTON FULL OF RAINCOATS! And TODAY'S QUESTION is: WHAT IS THE FIRST LETTER IN THE WORD **ZERO**?"

And to Guy Smiley's surprise, the Salesman ran away down the street shouting, "Hey, kid! Come back here with that letter!"

Sherlock Hemlock in The Mystery of the Missing Alphabet

Hmmmmmmm.
is may be harder than
ought. Perhaps you will
o me find all the letters
om A to Z. ZOUNDS!
'll solve this case yet!

Did you find ALL the letters?
Turn the page and see.